501

MUST-SEE MOVIES
MOVIE JOURNAL

Bounty
Books

This journal belongs to

NAME: _____

ADDRESS: _____

_____

TELEPHONE: _____

EMAIL: _____

Please return if found.
Thank you.

REVI

EWS

Title:

DIRECTOR:

DATE SEEN: _____

PERSONAL REVIEW: _____

_____

_____

_____

_____

_____

_____

_____

_____

_____

_____

_____

_____

_____

_____

_____

Title:

DIRECTOR:

DATE SEEN: _____

PERSONAL REVIEW: _____

_____

_____

_____

_____

_____

_____

_____

_____

_____

_____

_____

_____

_____

Star rating ☆ ☆ ☆ ☆ ☆

Title:

DIRECTOR:

DATE SEEN: _____

PERSONAL REVIEW: _____

_____

_____

_____

_____

_____

_____

_____

_____

_____

_____

_____

_____

_____

_____

Fred Astaire and Ginger Rogers in Top Hat

Title:

DIRECTOR:

DATE SEEN: _____

PERSONAL REVIEW: _____

_____

_____

_____

_____

_____

_____

_____

_____

_____

_____

_____

_____

_____

_____

Title:

DIRECTOR:

DATE SEEN: _____

PERSONAL REVIEW: _____

_____

_____

_____

_____

_____

_____

_____

_____

_____

_____

_____

_____

_____

_____

Star rating ☆ ☆ ☆ ☆ ☆

Title:

DIRECTOR:

DATE SEEN: _____

PERSONAL REVIEW: _____

_____

_____

_____

_____

_____

_____

_____

_____

_____

_____

_____

_____

_____

_____

Did you know? *When Stanley Kubrick released* The Shining *in 1980, audiences found it too slow, too long and fairly incomprehensible. Today it is regarded as a cinematic masterpiece, and the insane Jack Torrance is one of Jack Nicholson's best-known and -loved roles.*

Title:

DIRECTOR:

DATE SEEN: _____

PERSONAL REVIEW: _____

_____

_____

_____

_____

_____

_____

_____

_____

_____

_____

_____

_____

_____

_____

Jack Nicholson in The Shining

Star rating ☆ ☆ ☆ ☆ ☆

Title:

DIRECTOR:

DATE SEEN: _____

PERSONAL REVIEW: _____

_____

_____

_____

_____

_____

_____

_____

_____

_____

_____

_____

_____

_____

_____

Star rating ☆ ☆ ☆ ☆ ☆

Title:

DIRECTOR:

DATE SEEN: _____

PERSONAL REVIEW: _____

_____

_____

_____

_____

_____

_____

_____

_____

_____

_____

_____

_____

_____

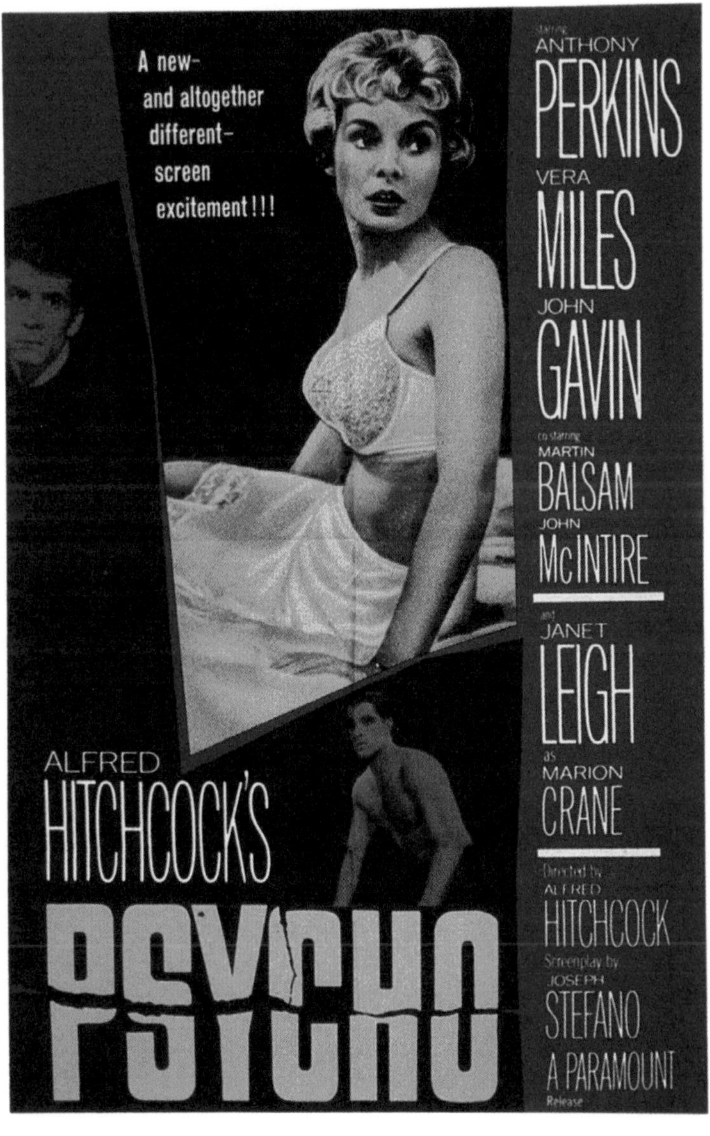

A new-
and altogether
different-
screen
excitement!!!
ANTHONY
PERKINS
VERA
MILES
JOHN
GAVIN
MARTIN
BALSAM
JOHN
McINTIRE
JANET
LEIGH
as
MARION
CRANE
ALFRED
HITCHCOCK'S
PSYCHO
Directed by
ALFRED
HITCHCOCK
Screenplay by
JOSEPH
STEFANO
A PARAMOUNT
Release

Title:

DIRECTOR:

DATE SEEN: _____

PERSONAL REVIEW: _____

_____

_____

_____

_____

_____

_____

_____

_____

_____

_____

_____

_____

_____

_____

_____

☆ ☆ ☆ ☆ ☆

Title:

DIRECTOR:

DATE SEEN: _____

PERSONAL REVIEW: _____

_____

_____

_____

_____

_____

_____

_____

_____

_____

_____

_____

_____

_____

Did you know?
America's most-rented video is The Sixth Sense, *a subtle, slow-paced horror movie starring Bruce Willis as a child psychologist. Over 80 million copies were rented in 2000 alone.*

☆ ☆ ☆ ☆ ☆

Title:

DIRECTOR:

DATE SEEN: _____

PERSONAL REVIEW: _____

Title:

DIRECTOR:

DATE SEEN: _____

PERSONAL REVIEW: _____

_____

_____

_____

_____

_____

_____

_____

_____

_____

_____

_____

_____

_____

_____

_____

Marlon Brando in The Godfather

Title:

DIRECTOR:

DATE SEEN: _____

PERSONAL REVIEW: _____

_____

_____

_____

_____

_____

_____

_____

_____

_____

_____

_____

_____

_____

☆ ☆ ☆ ☆ ☆

Title:

DIRECTOR:

DATE SEEN: _____

PERSONAL REVIEW: _____

_____

_____

_____

_____

_____

_____

_____

_____

_____

_____

_____

_____

_____

_____

Did you know? *In the 1982 comedy*
Tootsie, *Dustin Hoffman plays a young actor
who dresses up as a woman and auditions
for the role of Emily in a daytime soap. During
the making of the film, the crew realised that
if they had any bad news for Hoffman they
should wait until he was playing Emily
because he was 'much nicer as a woman'.*

Star rating ☆ ☆ ☆ ☆ ☆

Title:

DIRECTOR:

DATE SEEN:

PERSONAL REVIEW:

Title:

DIRECTOR:

DATE SEEN: _____

PERSONAL REVIEW: _____

_____

_____

_____

_____

_____

_____

_____

_____

_____

_____

_____

_____

_____

Title:

DIRECTOR:

DATE SEEN: _____

PERSONAL REVIEW: _____

_____

_____

_____

_____

_____

_____

_____

_____

_____

_____

_____

_____

_____

_____

_____

_____

Star rating ☆ ☆ ☆ ☆ ☆

Title:

DIRECTOR:

DATE SEEN: _____

PERSONAL REVIEW: _____

_____

_____

_____

_____

_____

_____

_____

_____

_____

_____

_____

_____

_____

_____

_____

Uma Thurman in Pulp Fiction

Star rating ☆ ☆ ☆ ☆ ☆

Title:

DIRECTOR:

DATE SEEN: _____

PERSONAL REVIEW: _____

_____

_____

_____

_____

_____

_____

_____

_____

_____

_____

_____

_____

_____

_____

Did you know? *The film* Gandhi *holds the record for the number of extras used. Made in 1982 before digital crowd scenes were possible, the film features 250,000 extras in a single scene.*

Star rating ☆ ☆ ☆ ☆ ☆

Title:

DIRECTOR:

DATE SEEN: _____

PERSONAL REVIEW: _____

_____

_____

_____

_____

_____

_____

_____

_____

_____

_____

_____

_____

_____

_____

Star rating ☆ ☆ ☆ ☆ ☆

Title:

DIRECTOR:

DATE SEEN: _____

PERSONAL REVIEW: _____

Title:

DIRECTOR:

DATE SEEN: _____

PERSONAL REVIEW: _____

_____

_____

_____

_____

_____

_____

_____

_____

_____

_____

_____

_____

_____

_____

Did you know? *When Grace Kelly played the role of Tracy Lord in* High Society *in 1956, she was soon to become Princess of Monaco, and the engagement ring she wears in the film is her own.*

Star rating ☆ ☆ ☆ ☆ ☆

Title:

DIRECTOR:

DATE SEEN: _____

PERSONAL REVIEW: _____

_____

_____

_____

_____

_____

_____

_____

_____

_____

_____

_____

_____

_____

_____

_____

Star rating ☆ ☆ ☆ ☆ ☆

Title:

DIRECTOR:

DATE SEEN: _____

PERSONAL REVIEW: _____

_____

_____

_____

_____

_____

_____

_____

_____

_____

_____

_____

_____

_____

_____

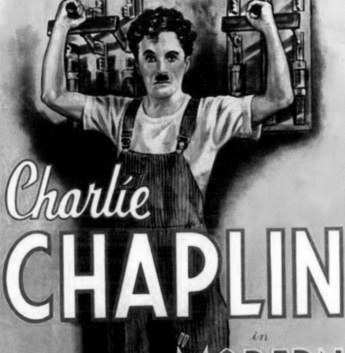

Charlie

CHAPLIN

in

"MODERN TIMES"

written, directed
and produced
by
CHARLES CHAPLIN

Released thru
UNITED
ARTISTS

Star rating  ☆ ☆ ☆ ☆ ☆

Title:

DIRECTOR:

DATE SEEN: _____

PERSONAL REVIEW: _____

_____

_____

_____

_____

_____

_____

_____

_____

_____

_____

_____

_____

_____

_____

_____

_____

Star rating ☆ ☆ ☆ ☆ ☆

Title:

DIRECTOR:

DATE SEEN: _____

PERSONAL REVIEW: _____

_____

_____

_____

_____

_____

_____

_____

_____

_____

_____

_____

_____

_____

_____

_____

Did you know? *The chariot-racing scenes in* Ben-Hur *last 20 minutes, but took three months to film on what was, in 1959, the largest single set ever constructed. The scenes still rank among the most iconic Hollywood moments.*

Title:

DIRECTOR:

DATE SEEN: _____

PERSONAL REVIEW: _____

_____

_____

_____

_____

_____

_____

_____

_____

_____

_____

_____

_____

_____

_____

_____

Star rating ☆ ☆ ☆ ☆ ☆

Title:

DIRECTOR:

DATE SEEN: _____

PERSONAL REVIEW: _____

_____

_____

_____

_____

_____

_____

_____

_____

_____

_____

_____

_____

_____

_____

Did you know? *In the 1949 comedy* Kind Hearts and Coronets, *Alec Guinness played eight different roles. All the characters are members of the d'Ascoyne family – a general, a cleric, an admiral, a banker, an amateur photographer, a duke, young Harry and his suffragette aunt, Lady Agatha – who are murdered one by one during the film.*

Star rating  ☆ ☆ ☆ ☆ ☆

Title:

DIRECTOR:

DATE SEEN: _____

PERSONAL REVIEW: _____

_____

_____

_____

_____

_____

_____

_____

_____

_____

_____

_____

_____

_____

_____

Star rating ☆ ☆ ☆ ☆ ☆

Title:

DIRECTOR:

DATE SEEN: _____

PERSONAL REVIEW: _____

_____

_____

_____

_____

_____

_____

_____

_____

_____

_____

_____

_____

_____

_____

_____

_____

Humphrey   Ingrid   Paul
BOGART · BERGMAN · HENREID

A
**HAL B. WALLIS
PRODUCTION**

"Casablanca"

CLAUDE   CONRAD   SYDNEY   PETER
RAINS · VEIDT · GREENSTREET · LORRE
Directed by **MICHAEL CURTIZ**

Star rating ☆ ☆ ☆ ☆ ☆

Title:

DIRECTOR:

DATE SEEN: _____

PERSONAL REVIEW: _____

_____

_____

_____

_____

_____

_____

_____

_____

_____

_____

_____

_____

_____

_____

Title:

DIRECTOR:

DATE SEEN: _____

PERSONAL REVIEW: _____

_____

_____

_____

_____

_____

_____

_____

_____

_____

_____

_____

_____

_____

Did you know? *Stanley Kubrick's 1971 film* A Clockwork Orange *was never actually banned, it was withdrawn from release in the UK at the request of the director after his family received death threats. The film was accused of inciting violence.*

Star rating ☆ ☆ ☆ ☆ ☆

Title:

DIRECTOR:

DATE SEEN: _____

PERSONAL REVIEW: _____

_____

_____

_____

_____

_____

_____

_____

_____

_____

_____

_____

_____

_____

_____

_____

Star rating ☆ ☆ ☆ ☆ ☆

Title:

DIRECTOR:

DATE SEEN: _____

PERSONAL REVIEW: _____

_____

_____

_____

_____

_____

_____

_____

_____

_____

_____

_____

_____

_____

_____

_____

 ☆ ☆ ☆ ☆ ☆

Title:

DIRECTOR:

DATE SEEN: _____

PERSONAL REVIEW: _____

_____

_____

_____

_____

_____

_____

_____

_____

_____

_____

_____

_____

_____

_____

Did you know? *The commentary, begrudgingly recorded by Harrison Ford for the original version of* Blade Runner *(1982) was insisted upon by the distributor. It was dropped by Ridley Scott in the 1991 director's cut.*

Title:

DIRECTOR:

DATE SEEN: _____

PERSONAL REVIEW: _____

_____

_____

_____

_____

_____

_____

_____

_____

_____

_____

_____

_____

_____

_____

JAMES STEWART
KIM NOVAK
IN ALFRED HITCHCOCK'S

'VERTIGO'

BARBARA BEL GEDDES TOM HELMORE HENRY JONES ALFRED HITCHCOCK ALEC COPPEL & SAMUEL TAYLOR TECHNICOLOR
BASED UPON THE NOVEL D'ENTRE LES MORTS BY PIERRE BOILEAU AND THOMAS NARCEJAC MUSIC BY BERNARD HERRMANN

Title:

DIRECTOR:

DATE SEEN: _____

PERSONAL REVIEW: _____

_____

_____

_____

_____

_____

_____

_____

_____

_____

_____

_____

_____

_____

Title:

DIRECTOR:

DATE SEEN:

PERSONAL REVIEW:

Did you know? *The opening sequence of* The Sound of Music *nearly didn't happen. The helicopter holding the camera knocked Julie Andrews off her feet every time it panned over the hillside on which she was standing.*

Title:

DIRECTOR:

DATE SEEN: _____

PERSONAL REVIEW: _____

_____

_____

_____

_____

_____

_____

_____

_____

_____

_____

_____

_____

_____

_____

_____

Title:

DIRECTOR:

DATE SEEN: _____

PERSONAL REVIEW: _____

_____

_____

_____

_____

_____

_____

_____

_____

_____

_____

_____

_____

_____

_____

Title:

DIRECTOR:

DATE SEEN: _____

PERSONAL REVIEW: _____

_____

_____

_____

_____

_____

_____

_____

_____

_____

_____

_____

_____

_____

Title:

DIRECTOR:

DATE SEEN: _____

PERSONAL REVIEW: _____

_____

_____

_____

_____

_____

_____

_____

_____

_____

_____

_____

_____

_____

_____

_____

_____

La Compagnie Mirisch présente

Steve McQueen
Faye Dunaway

un film de Norman Jewison

L'affaire Thomas Crown
(THE THOMAS CROWN AFFAIR)

et avec Paul Burke   Jack Weston   TECHNICOLOR®

Musique Michel Legrand · Écrit par Alan R. Trustman
Produit et réalisé par Norman Jewison · Distribué par Les Artistes Associés

United Artists

Title:

DIRECTOR:

DATE SEEN: _____

PERSONAL REVIEW: _____

_____

_____

_____

_____

_____

_____

_____

_____

_____

_____

_____

_____

_____

_____

Star rating ☆ ☆ ☆ ☆ ☆

Title:

DIRECTOR:

DATE SEEN: _____

PERSONAL REVIEW: _____

_____

_____

_____

_____

_____

_____

_____

_____

_____

_____

_____

_____

_____

_____

Did you know? *During the filming of* Wuthering Heights *in 1939, Lawrence Olivier was dragged away from London and his new fiancée Vivien Leigh. It must have been difficult when he was passed over for the Best Actor Oscar while she won Best Actress for* Gone with the Wind.

Star rating ☆ ☆ ☆ ☆ ☆

Title:

DIRECTOR:

DATE SEEN: _____

PERSONAL REVIEW: _____

_____

_____

_____

_____

_____

_____

_____

_____

_____

_____

_____

_____

_____

_____

_____

Star rating ☆ ☆ ☆ ☆ ☆

Title:

DIRECTOR:

DATE SEEN:

PERSONAL REVIEW:

Title:

DIRECTOR:

DATE SEEN: _____

PERSONAL REVIEW: _____

_____

_____

_____

_____

_____

_____

_____

_____

_____

_____

_____

_____

_____

Star rating ☆ ☆ ☆ ☆ ☆

Title:

DIRECTOR:

DATE SEEN: _____

PERSONAL REVIEW: _____

_____

_____

_____

_____

_____

_____

_____

_____

_____

_____

_____

_____

_____

_____

_____

Title:

DIRECTOR:

DATE SEEN: _____

PERSONAL REVIEW: _____

_____

_____

_____

_____

_____

_____

_____

_____

_____

_____

_____

_____

_____

_____

Title:

DIRECTOR:

DATE SEEN:

PERSONAL REVIEW:

Did you know? *Writer Dalton Trumbo was blacklisted as one of the Hollywood Ten for alleged un-American activities. When* Roman Holiday *won the Oscar for Best Screenplay, his friend Ian McLellan Hunter took credit for the story and accepted the award.*

Star rating ☆ ☆ ☆ ☆ ☆

Title:

DIRECTOR:

DATE SEEN: _____

PERSONAL REVIEW: _____

_____

_____

_____

_____

_____

_____

_____

_____

_____

_____

_____

_____

_____

_____

_____

☆ ☆ ☆ ☆ ☆

Title:

DIRECTOR:

DATE SEEN: _____

PERSONAL REVIEW: _____

_____

_____

_____

_____

_____

_____

_____

_____

_____

_____

_____

_____

_____

_____

Tony Curtis and Marilyn Monroe in Some Like it Hot

Title:

DIRECTOR:

DATE SEEN: _____

PERSONAL REVIEW: _____

_____

_____

_____

_____

_____

_____

_____

_____

_____

_____

_____

_____

_____

_____

_____

_____

Title:

DIRECTOR:

DATE SEEN: _____

PERSONAL REVIEW: _____

_____

_____

_____

_____

_____

_____

_____

_____

_____

_____

_____

_____

_____

_____

**Did you know?** The author of the novel Breakfast at Tiffany's, _Truman Capote, wanted Marilyn Monroe to play the film role of Holly Golightly. Her drama coach dissuaded her, however, as he thought the role of a call girl would not fit with her new image. The role was played by Audrey Hepburn who admitted that she, too, felt she had been miscast._

Title:

DIRECTOR:

DATE SEEN: _____

PERSONAL REVIEW: _____

_____

_____

_____

_____

_____

_____

_____

_____

_____

_____

_____

_____

_____

_____

Title:

DIRECTOR:

DATE SEEN: _____

PERSONAL REVIEW: _____

_____

_____

_____

_____

_____

_____

_____

_____

_____

_____

_____

_____

_____

_____

Gene Kelly promotes Singin' in the Rain.

Title:

DIRECTOR:

DATE SEEN: _____

PERSONAL REVIEW: _____

_____

_____

_____

_____

_____

_____

_____

_____

_____

_____

_____

_____

_____

_____

_____

movie

SILENT

MOVIES LENT

Movie	LENT TO	DATE	RETURNED
			☐
			☐
			☐
			☐
			☐
			☐
			☐
			☐
			☐
			☐
			☐
			☐
			☐
			☐
			☐
			☐
			☐
			☐
			☐
			☐

Movie	LENT TO	DATE	RETURNED
			☐
			☐
			☐
			☐
			☐
			☐
			☐
			☐
			☐
			☐
			☐
			☐
			☐
			☐
			☐
			☐
			☐
			☐
			☐
			☐

MOVIES LENT

Movie	LENT TO	DATE	RETURNED
			☐
			☐
			☐
			☐
			☐
			☐
			☐
			☐
			☐
			☐
			☐
			☐
			☐
			☐
			☐
			☐
			☐
			☐
			☐
			☐

Mena Suvari in American Beauty

MOVIES LENT

Movie	LENT TO	DATE	RETURNED
			☐
			☐
			☐
			☐
			☐
			☐
			☐
			☐
			☐
			☐
			☐
			☐
			☐
			☐
			☐
			☐
			☐
			☐
			☐
			☐

Movie	LENT TO	DATE	RETURNED
			☐
			☐
			☐
			☐
			☐
			☐
			☐
			☐
			☐
			☐
			☐
			☐
			☐
			☐
			☐
			☐
			☐
			☐
			☐
			☐

MOVIES LENT

Movie	LENT TO	DATE	RETURNED
			☐
			☐
			☐
			☐
			☐
			☐
			☐
			☐
			☐
			☐
			☐
			☐
			☐
			☐
			☐
			☐
			☐
			☐
			☐
			☐

Movie	LENT TO	DATE	RETURNED
			☐
			☐
			☐
			☐
			☐
			☐
			☐
			☐
			☐
			☐
			☐
			☐
			☐
			☐
			☐
			☐
			☐
			☐
			☐
			☐

MOVIES LENT

Movie	LENT TO	DATE	RETURNED
			☐
			☐
			☐
			☐
			☐
			☐
			☐
			☐
			☐
			☐
			☐
			☐
			☐
			☐
			☐
			☐
			☐
			☐
			☐
			☐
			☐

Movie	LENT TO	DATE	RETURNED
			☐
			☐
			☐
			☐
			☐
			☐
			☐
			☐
			☐
			☐
			☐
			☐
			☐
			☐
			☐
			☐
			☐
			☐
			☐
			☐

MOVIES LENT

Movie	LENT TO	DATE	RETURNED
			☐
			☐
			☐
			☐
			☐
			☐
			☐
			☐
			☐
			☐
			☐
			☐
			☐
			☐
			☐
			☐
			☐
			☐
			☐
			☐

MOVIES LENT

Movie	LENT TO	DATE	RETURNED
			☐
			☐
			☐
			☐
			☐
			☐
			☐
			☐
			☐
			☐
			☐
			☐
			☐
			☐
			☐
			☐
			☐
			☐
			☐
			☐

Movie	LENT TO	DATE	RETURNED
			☐
			☐
			☐
			☐
			☐
			☐
			☐
			☐
			☐
			☐
			☐
			☐
			☐
			☐
			☐
			☐
			☐
			☐
			☐
			☐

MOVIES LENT

Movie	LENT TO	DATE	RETURNED
			☐
			☐
			☐
			☐
			☐
			☐
			☐
			☐
			☐
			☐
			☐
			☐
			☐
			☐
			☐
			☐
			☐
			☐
			☐
			☐

Movie	LENT TO	DATE	RETURNED
			☐
			☐
			☐
			☐
			☐
			☐
			☐
			☐
			☐
			☐
			☐
			☐
			☐
			☐
			☐
			☐
			☐
			☐
			☐
			☐

MOVIES LENT

Movie	LENT TO	DATE	RETURNED
			☐
			☐
			☐
			☐
			☐
			☐
			☐
			☐
			☐
			☐
			☐
			☐
			☐
			☐
			☐
			☐
			☐
			☐
			☐

Movie	LENT TO	DATE	RETURNED
			☐
			☐
			☐
			☐
			☐
			☐
			☐
			☐
			☐
			☐
			☐
			☐
			☐
			☐
			☐
			☐
			☐
			☐
			☐

MOVIES LENT

Movie	LENT TO	DATE	RETURNED
			☐
			☐
			☐
			☐
			☐
			☐
			☐
			☐
			☐
			☐
			☐
			☐
			☐
			☐
			☐
			☐
			☐
			☐
			☐
			☐

Jack Haley, Ray Bolger, Judy Garland and Bert Lahr promote The Wizard of Oz.

MOVIES LENT

Movie	LENT TO	DATE	RETURNED
			☐
			☐
			☐
			☐
			☐
			☐
			☐
			☐
			☐
			☐
			☐
			☐
			☐
			☐
			☐
			☐
			☐
			☐
			☐

Movie	LENT TO	DATE	RETURNED
			☐
			☐
			☐
			☐
			☐
			☐
			☐
			☐
			☐
			☐
			☐
			☐
			☐
			☐
			☐
			☐
			☐
			☐
			☐
			☐

MOVIES LENT

Movie	LENT TO	DATE	RETURNED
			☐
			☐
			☐
			☐
			☐
			☐
			☐
			☐
			☐
			☐
			☐
			☐
			☐
			☐
			☐
			☐
			☐
			☐
			☐
			☐

Movie	LENT TO	DATE	RETURNED
			☐
			☐
			☐
			☐
			☐
			☐
			☐
			☐
			☐
			☐
			☐
			☐
			☐
			☐
			☐
			☐
			☐
			☐
			☐
			☐

MOVIES LENT

Movie	LENT TO	DATE	RETURNED
			☐
			☐
			☐
			☐
			☐
			☐
			☐
			☐
			☐
			☐
			☐
			☐
			☐
			☐
			☐
			☐
			☐
			☐
			☐

Movie	LENT TO	DATE	RETURNED
			☐
			☐
			☐
			☐
			☐
			☐
			☐
			☐
			☐
			☐
			☐
			☐
			☐
			☐
			☐
			☐
			☐
			☐
			☐
			☐

MOVIES LENT

Movie	LENT TO	DATE	RETURNED
			☐
			☐
			☐
			☐
			☐
			☐
			☐
			☐
			☐
			☐
			☐
			☐
			☐
			☐
			☐
			☐
			☐
			☐
			☐
			☐

Claire Danes in William Shakespeare's Romeo and Juliet

MOVIES LENT

Movie	LENT TO	DATE	RETURNED
			☐
			☐
			☐
			☐
			☐
			☐
			☐
			☐
			☐
			☐
			☐
			☐
			☐
			☐
			☐
			☐
			☐
			☐
			☐
			☐
			☐

Movie	LENT TO	DATE	RETURNED
			☐
			☐
			☐
			☐
			☐
			☐
			☐
			☐
			☐
			☐
			☐
			☐
			☐
			☐
			☐
			☐
			☐
			☐
			☐
			☐

BORRO

movies

MOVIES BORROWED

Movie	BORROWED FROM	DATE	RETURNED
			☐
			☐
			☐
			☐
			☐
			☐
			☐
			☐
			☐
			☐
			☐
			☐
			☐
			☐
			☐
			☐
			☐
			☐
			☐
			☐

MOVIES BORROWED

Movie	BORROWED FROM	DATE	RETURNED
			☐
			☐
			☐
			☐
			☐
			☐
			☐
			☐
			☐
			☐
			☐
			☐
			☐
			☐
			☐
			☐
			☐
			☐
			☐
			☐

MOVIES BORROWED

Movie	BORROWED FROM	DATE	RETURNED
			☐
			☐
			☐
			☐
			☐
			☐
			☐
			☐
			☐
			☐
			☐
			☐
			☐
			☐
			☐
			☐
			☐
			☐
			☐
			☐

MOVIES BORROWED

Movie	BORROWED FROM	DATE	RETURNED
			☐
			☐
			☐
			☐
			☐
			☐
			☐
			☐
			☐
			☐
			☐
			☐
			☐
			☐
			☐
			☐
			☐
			☐
			☐
			☐

MOVIES BORROWED

Movie	BORROWED FROM	DATE	RETURNED
			☐
			☐
			☐
			☐
			☐
			☐
			☐
			☐
			☐
			☐
			☐
			☐
			☐
			☐
			☐
			☐
			☐
			☐
			☐

Movie	BORROWED FROM	DATE	RETURNED
			☐
			☐
			☐
			☐
			☐
			☐
			☐
			☐
			☐
			☐
			☐
			☐
			☐
			☐
			☐
			☐
			☐
			☐
			☐
			☐

MOVIES BORROWED

Movie	BORROWED FROM	DATE	RETURNED
			☐
			☐
			☐
			☐
			☐
			☐
			☐
			☐
			☐
			☐
			☐
			☐
			☐
			☐
			☐
			☐
			☐
			☐
			☐
			☐

Joan Crawford and Bette Davis in Whatever Happened to Baby Jane?

MOVIES BORROWED

Movie	BORROWED FROM	DATE	RETURNED
			☐
			☐
			☐
			☐
			☐
			☐
			☐
			☐
			☐
			☐
			☐
			☐
			☐
			☐
			☐
			☐
			☐
			☐
			☐

Movie	BORROWED FROM	DATE	RETURNED
			☐
			☐
			☐
			☐
			☐
			☐
			☐
			☐
			☐
			☐
			☐
			☐
			☐
			☐
			☐
			☐
			☐
			☐
			☐
			☐

MOVIES BORROWED

Movie	BORROWED FROM	DATE	RETURNED
			☐
			☐
			☐
			☐
			☐
			☐
			☐
			☐
			☐
			☐
			☐
			☐
			☐
			☐
			☐
			☐
			☐
			☐
			☐
			☐

MOVIES BORROWED

Movie	BORROWED FROM	DATE	RETURNED
			☐
			☐
			☐
			☐
			☐
			☐
			☐
			☐
			☐
			☐
			☐
			☐
			☐
			☐
			☐
			☐
			☐
			☐
			☐
			☐

MOVIES BORROWED

Movie	BORROWED FROM	DATE	RETURNED
			☐
			☐
			☐
			☐
			☐
			☐
			☐
			☐
			☐
			☐
			☐
			☐
			☐
			☐
			☐
			☐
			☐
			☐
			☐
			☐

Movie

Movie	BORROWED FROM	DATE	RETURNED
			☐
			☐
			☐
			☐
			☐
			☐
			☐
			☐
			☐
			☐
			☐
			☐
			☐
			☐
			☐
			☐
			☐
			☐
			☐
			☐

MOVIES BORROWED

Movie	BORROWED FROM	DATE	RETURNED
			☐
			☐
			☐
			☐
			☐
			☐
			☐
			☐
			☐
			☐
			☐
			☐
			☐
			☐
			☐
			☐
			☐
			☐
			☐
			☐

Burt Lancaster and Deborah Kerr in From Here to Eternity

MOVIES BORROWED

Movie	BORROWED FROM	DATE	RETURNED
			☐
			☐
			☐
			☐
			☐
			☐
			☐
			☐
			☐
			☐
			☐
			☐
			☐
			☐
			☐
			☐
			☐
			☐
			☐
			☐

Movie	BORROWED FROM	DATE	RETURNED
			☐
			☐
			☐
			☐
			☐
			☐
			☐
			☐
			☐
			☐
			☐
			☐
			☐
			☐
			☐
			☐
			☐
			☐
			☐
			☐

MOVIES BORROWED

Movie	BORROWED FROM	DATE	RETURNED
			☐
			☐
			☐
			☐
			☐
			☐
			☐
			☐
			☐
			☐
			☐
			☐
			☐
			☐
			☐
			☐
			☐
			☐
			☐
			☐

Movie	BORROWED FROM	DATE	RETURNED
			☐
			☐
			☐
			☐
			☐
			☐
			☐
			☐
			☐
			☐
			☐
			☐
			☐
			☐
			☐
			☐
			☐
			☐
			☐
			☐

MOVIES BORROWED

Movie	BORROWED FROM	DATE	RETURNED
			☐
			☐
			☐
			☐
			☐
			☐
			☐
			☐
			☐
			☐
			☐
			☐
			☐
			☐
			☐
			☐
			☐
			☐
			☐
			☐

Movie	BORROWED FROM	DATE	RETURNED
			☐
			☐
			☐
			☐
			☐
			☐
			☐
			☐
			☐
			☐
			☐
			☐
			☐
			☐
			☐
			☐
			☐
			☐
			☐
			☐

MOVIES BORROWED

Movie	BORROWED FROM	DATE	RETURNED
			☐
			☐
			☐
			☐
			☐
			☐
			☐
			☐
			☐
			☐
			☐
			☐
			☐
			☐
			☐
			☐
			☐
			☐
			☐
			☐

GARY COOPER
GRACE KELLY
GARY COOPER
TOMAS MITCHELL
LLOYD BRIDGES
KATY JURADO
GRACE KELLY
OTTO KRUGER
LON CHANEY
HENRY MORGAN
-PRODUCTION-
STANLEY
KRAMER
HIGH
SI TOI AUSSI TU M'ABANDONNES
NOON
MUSIQUE
de
DIMITRI TIOMKIN
-REGIE-
FRED ZINNEMANN
LE TRAIN SIFFLERA 3 FOIS

MOVIES BORROWED

Movie	BORROWED FROM	DATE	RETURNED
			☐
			☐
			☐
			☐
			☐
			☐
			☐
			☐
			☐
			☐
			☐
			☐
			☐
			☐
			☐
			☐
			☐
			☐
			☐
			☐

Movie	BORROWED FROM	DATE	RETURNED
			☐
			☐
			☐
			☐
			☐
			☐
			☐
			☐
			☐
			☐
			☐
			☐
			☐
			☐
			☐
			☐
			☐
			☐
			☐
			☐

MOVIES BORROWED

Movie	BORROWED FROM	DATE	RETURNED
			☐
			☐
			☐
			☐
			☐
			☐
			☐
			☐
			☐
			☐
			☐
			☐
			☐
			☐
			☐
			☐
			☐
			☐
			☐
			☐

Movie	BORROWED FROM	DATE	RETURNED
			☐
			☐
			☐
			☐
			☐
			☐
			☐
			☐
			☐
			☐
			☐
			☐
			☐
			☐
			☐
			☐
			☐
			☐
			☐
			☐

MOVIES BORROWED

Movie	BORROWED FROM	DATE	RETURNED
			☐
			☐
			☐
			☐
			☐
			☐
			☐
			☐
			☐
			☐
			☐
			☐
			☐
			☐
			☐
			☐
			☐
			☐
			☐

Movie	BORROWED FROM	DATE	RETURNED
			☐
			☐
			☐
			☐
			☐
			☐
			☐
			☐
			☐
			☐
			☐
			☐
			☐
			☐
			☐
			☐
			☐
			☐
			☐
			☐

viewin
WISl

gALIST

VIEWING WISHLIST

Movie:

DIRECTOR:

RECOMMENDED BY:

SEEN ☐

Movie:

DIRECTOR:

RECOMMENDED BY:

SEEN ☐

Movie:

DIRECTOR:

RECOMMENDED BY:

SEEN ☐

Movie:

DIRECTOR:

RECOMMENDED BY:

SEEN ☐

Movie:

DIRECTOR:

RECOMMENDED BY:

SEEN ☐

Movie:

DIRECTOR:

RECOMMENDED BY:

SEEN ☐

Movie:

DIRECTOR:

RECOMMENDED BY:

SEEN ☐

Movie:

DIRECTOR:

RECOMMENDED BY:

SEEN ☐

Movie:

DIRECTOR:

RECOMMENDED BY:

SEEN ☐

Movie:

DIRECTOR:

RECOMMENDED BY:

SEEN ☐

VIEWING WISHLIST

Movie:

DIRECTOR:

RECOMMENDED BY:

SEEN ☐

Movie:

DIRECTOR:

RECOMMENDED BY:

SEEN ☐

Movie:

DIRECTOR:

RECOMMENDED BY:

SEEN ☐

Movie:

DIRECTOR:

RECOMMENDED BY:

SEEN ☐

Movie:

DIRECTOR:

RECOMMENDED BY:

SEEN ☐

Alec Guinness in The Bridge on the River Kwai

VIEWING WISHLIST

Movie:

DIRECTOR:

RECOMMENDED BY:

SEEN ☐

Movie:

DIRECTOR:

RECOMMENDED BY:

SEEN ☐

Movie:

DIRECTOR:

RECOMMENDED BY:

SEEN ☐

Movie:

DIRECTOR:

RECOMMENDED BY:

SEEN ☐

Movie:

DIRECTOR:

RECOMMENDED BY:

SEEN ☐

Movie: _____

DIRECTOR: _____

RECOMMENDED BY: _____

_____ SEEN ☐

Movie: _____

DIRECTOR: _____

RECOMMENDED BY: _____

_____ SEEN ☐

Movie: _____

DIRECTOR: _____

RECOMMENDED BY: _____

_____ SEEN ☐

Movie: _____

DIRECTOR: _____

RECOMMENDED BY: _____

_____ SEEN ☐

Movie: _____

DIRECTOR: _____

RECOMMENDED BY: _____

_____ SEEN ☐

Movie:

DIRECTOR:

RECOMMENDED BY:

SEEN ☐

Movie:

DIRECTOR:

RECOMMENDED BY:

SEEN ☐

Movie:

DIRECTOR:

RECOMMENDED BY:

SEEN ☐

Movie:

DIRECTOR:

RECOMMENDED BY:

SEEN ☐

Movie:

DIRECTOR:

RECOMMENDED BY:

SEEN ☐

VIEWING WISHLIST

Movie:

DIRECTOR:

RECOMMENDED BY:

SEEN ☐

Movie:

DIRECTOR:

RECOMMENDED BY:

SEEN ☐

Movie:

DIRECTOR:

RECOMMENDED BY:

SEEN ☐

Movie:

DIRECTOR:

RECOMMENDED BY:

SEEN ☐

Movie:

DIRECTOR:

RECOMMENDED BY:

SEEN ☐

VIEWING WISHLIST

Movie:

DIRECTOR:

RECOMMENDED BY:

SEEN ☐

Movie:

DIRECTOR:

RECOMMENDED BY:

SEEN ☐

Movie:

DIRECTOR:

RECOMMENDED BY:

SEEN ☐

Movie:

DIRECTOR:

RECOMMENDED BY:

SEEN ☐

Movie:

DIRECTOR:

RECOMMENDED BY:

SEEN ☐

Movie: _____

DIRECTOR: _____

RECOMMENDED BY: _____

_____ SEEN ☐

Movie: _____

DIRECTOR: _____

RECOMMENDED BY: _____

_____ SEEN ☐

Movie: _____

DIRECTOR: _____

RECOMMENDED BY: _____

_____ SEEN ☐

Movie: _____

DIRECTOR: _____

RECOMMENDED BY: _____

_____ SEEN ☐

Movie: _____

DIRECTOR: _____

RECOMMENDED BY: _____

_____ SEEN ☐

Movie: _____

DIRECTOR: _____

RECOMMENDED BY: _____

_____ SEEN ☐

Movie: _____

DIRECTOR: _____

RECOMMENDED BY: _____

_____ SEEN ☐

Movie: _____

DIRECTOR: _____

RECOMMENDED BY: _____

_____ SEEN ☐

Movie: _____

DIRECTOR: _____

RECOMMENDED BY: _____

_____ SEEN ☐

Movie: _____

DIRECTOR: _____

RECOMMENDED BY: _____

_____ SEEN ☐

JOSEPH E. LEVINE
PRESENTS
A
MIKE NICHOLS
LAWRENCE TURMAN
PRODUCTION

This
is
Benjamin.

He's
a little
worried
about
his
future.

THE GRADUATE

STARRING
ANNE BANCROFT AND **DUSTIN HOFFMAN** · **KATHARINE ROSS**
SCREENPLAY BY   SONGS BY
CALDER WILLINGHAM AND **BUCK HENRY**   **PAUL SIMON**
PERFORMED BY   PRODUCED BY
SIMON AND **GARFUNKEL**   **LAWRENCE TURMAN**
DIRECTED BY
MIKE NICHOLS TECHNICOLOR® PANAVISION®

Movie:

DIRECTOR:

RECOMMENDED BY:

SEEN ☐

Movie:

DIRECTOR:

RECOMMENDED BY:

SEEN ☐

Movie:

DIRECTOR:

RECOMMENDED BY:

SEEN ☐

Movie:

DIRECTOR:

RECOMMENDED BY:

SEEN ☐

Movie:

DIRECTOR:

RECOMMENDED BY:

SEEN ☐

Movie:

DIRECTOR:

RECOMMENDED BY:

SEEN ☐

Movie:

DIRECTOR:

RECOMMENDED BY:

SEEN ☐

Movie:

DIRECTOR:

RECOMMENDED BY:

SEEN ☐

Movie:

DIRECTOR:

RECOMMENDED BY:

SEEN ☐

Movie:

DIRECTOR:

RECOMMENDED BY:

SEEN ☐

VIEWING WISHLIST

Movie: _____

DIRECTOR: _____

RECOMMENDED BY: _____

_____ SEEN ☐

Movie: _____

DIRECTOR: _____

RECOMMENDED BY: _____

_____ SEEN ☐

Movie: _____

DIRECTOR: _____

RECOMMENDED BY: _____

_____ SEEN ☐

Movie: _____

DIRECTOR: _____

RECOMMENDED BY: _____

_____ SEEN ☐

Movie: _____

DIRECTOR: _____

RECOMMENDED BY: _____

_____ SEEN ☐

Movie:

DIRECTOR:

RECOMMENDED BY:

SEEN ☐

Movie:

DIRECTOR:

RECOMMENDED BY:

SEEN ☐

Movie:

DIRECTOR:

RECOMMENDED BY:

SEEN ☐

Movie:

DIRECTOR:

RECOMMENDED BY:

SEEN ☐

Movie:

DIRECTOR:

RECOMMENDED BY:

SEEN ☐

Movie:

DIRECTOR:

RECOMMENDED BY:

SEEN ☐

Movie:

DIRECTOR:

RECOMMENDED BY:

SEEN ☐

Movie:

DIRECTOR:

RECOMMENDED BY:

SEEN ☐

Movie:

DIRECTOR:

RECOMMENDED BY:

SEEN ☐

Movie:

DIRECTOR:

RECOMMENDED BY:

SEEN ☐

Movie:

DIRECTOR:

RECOMMENDED BY:

SEEN ☐

Movie:

DIRECTOR:

RECOMMENDED BY:

SEEN ☐

Movie:

DIRECTOR:

RECOMMENDED BY:

SEEN ☐

Movie:

DIRECTOR:

RECOMMENDED BY:

SEEN ☐

Movie:

DIRECTOR:

RECOMMENDED BY:

SEEN ☐

Movie:

DIRECTOR:

RECOMMENDED BY:

SEEN ☐

Movie:

DIRECTOR:

RECOMMENDED BY:

SEEN ☐

Movie:

DIRECTOR:

RECOMMENDED BY:

SEEN ☐

Movie:

DIRECTOR:

RECOMMENDED BY:

SEEN ☐

Movie:

DIRECTOR:

RECOMMENDED BY:

SEEN ☐

Audrey Hepburn in Breakfast at Tiffany's

Movie:

DIRECTOR:

RECOMMENDED BY:

SEEN

Movie:

DIRECTOR:

RECOMMENDED BY:

SEEN

Movie:

DIRECTOR:

RECOMMENDED BY:

SEEN

Movie:

DIRECTOR:

RECOMMENDED BY:

SEEN

Movie:

DIRECTOR:

RECOMMENDED BY:

SEEN

Movie:

DIRECTOR:

RECOMMENDED BY:

SEEN ☐

Movie:

DIRECTOR:

RECOMMENDED BY:

SEEN ☐

Movie:

DIRECTOR:

RECOMMENDED BY:

SEEN ☐

Movie:

DIRECTOR:

RECOMMENDED BY:

SEEN ☐

Movie:

DIRECTOR:

RECOMMENDED BY:

SEEN ☐

VIEWING WISHLIST

Movie:

DIRECTOR:

RECOMMENDED BY:

SEEN ☐

Movie:

DIRECTOR:

RECOMMENDED BY:

SEEN ☐

Movie:

DIRECTOR:

RECOMMENDED BY:

SEEN ☐

Movie:

DIRECTOR:

RECOMMENDED BY:

SEEN ☐

Movie:

DIRECTOR:

RECOMMENDED BY:

SEEN ☐

SACRIFICE

Movie:

DIRECTOR:

RECOMMENDED BY:

SEEN ☐

Movie:

DIRECTOR:

RECOMMENDED BY:

SEEN ☐

Movie:

DIRECTOR:

RECOMMENDED BY:

SEEN ☐

Movie:

DIRECTOR:

RECOMMENDED BY:

SEEN ☐

Movie:

DIRECTOR:

RECOMMENDED BY:

SEEN ☐

Movie:

DIRECTOR:

RECOMMENDED BY:

SEEN ☐

Movie:

DIRECTOR:

RECOMMENDED BY:

SEEN ☐

Movie:

DIRECTOR:

RECOMMENDED BY:

SEEN ☐

Movie:

DIRECTOR:

RECOMMENDED BY:

SEEN ☐

Movie:

DIRECTOR:

RECOMMENDED BY:

SEEN ☐

Movie:

DIRECTOR:

RECOMMENDED BY:

SEEN ☐

Movie:

DIRECTOR:

RECOMMENDED BY:

SEEN ☐

Movie:

DIRECTOR:

RECOMMENDED BY:

SEEN ☐

Movie:

DIRECTOR:

RECOMMENDED BY:

SEEN ☐

Movie:

DIRECTOR:

RECOMMENDED BY:

SEEN ☐

Movie:

DIRECTOR:

RECOMMENDED BY:

SEEN ☐

Movie:

DIRECTOR:

RECOMMENDED BY:

SEEN ☐

Movie:

DIRECTOR:

RECOMMENDED BY:

SEEN ☐

Movie:

DIRECTOR:

RECOMMENDED BY:

SEEN ☐

Movie:

DIRECTOR:

RECOMMENDED BY:

SEEN ☐

VIEWING WISHLIST

Movie:

DIRECTOR:

RECOMMENDED BY:

SEEN ☐

Movie:

DIRECTOR:

RECOMMENDED BY:

SEEN ☐

Movie:

DIRECTOR:

RECOMMENDED BY:

SEEN ☐

Movie:

DIRECTOR:

RECOMMENDED BY:

SEEN ☐

Movie:

DIRECTOR:

RECOMMENDED BY:

SEEN ☐

Movie:

DIRECTOR:

RECOMMENDED BY:

SEEN ☐

Movie:

DIRECTOR:

RECOMMENDED BY:

SEEN ☐

Movie:

DIRECTOR:

RECOMMENDED BY:

SEEN ☐

Movie:

DIRECTOR:

RECOMMENDED BY:

SEEN ☐

Movie:

DIRECTOR:

RECOMMENDED BY:

SEEN ☐

VIEWING WISHLIST

Movie:

DIRECTOR:

RECOMMENDED BY:

SEEN ☐

Movie:

DIRECTOR:

RECOMMENDED BY:

SEEN ☐

Movie:

DIRECTOR:

RECOMMENDED BY:

SEEN ☐

Movie:

DIRECTOR:

RECOMMENDED BY:

SEEN ☐

Movie:

DIRECTOR:

RECOMMENDED BY:

SEEN ☐

en association avec SEVEN ARTS PRODUCTIONS **LOLITA** de JAMES B. HARRIS et STANLEY KUBRICK

JAMES MASON · SHELLEY WINTERS · PETER SELLERS

et **SUE LYON** dans le rôle de "Lolita"

Réalisation: **STANLEY KUBRICK** · Scénario: **VLADIMIR NABOKOV** · Production: **JAMES B. HARRIS**

d'après le roman "Lolita"

VIEWING WISHLIST

Movie:

DIRECTOR:

RECOMMENDED BY:

SEEN ☐

Movie:

DIRECTOR:

RECOMMENDED BY:

SEEN ☐

Movie:

DIRECTOR:

RECOMMENDED BY:

SEEN ☐

Movie:

DIRECTOR:

RECOMMENDED BY:

SEEN ☐

Movie:

DIRECTOR:

RECOMMENDED BY:

SEEN ☐

Movie: _____

DIRECTOR: _____

RECOMMENDED BY: _____

_____ SEEN ☐

Movie: _____

DIRECTOR: _____

RECOMMENDED BY: _____

_____ SEEN ☐

Movie: _____

DIRECTOR: _____

RECOMMENDED BY: _____

_____ SEEN ☐

Movie: _____

DIRECTOR: _____

RECOMMENDED BY: _____

_____ SEEN ☐

Movie: _____

DIRECTOR: _____

RECOMMENDED BY: _____

_____ SEEN ☐

CHEC

501
MUST-SEE MOVIES

KLIST

501 MUST-SEE MOVIES CHECKLIST

- [ ] `À bout de souffle
- [ ] Ace in the Hole
- [ ] Adam's Rib
- [ ] Adventures of Robin Hood, The
- [ ] Affair to Remember, An
- [ ] African Queen, The
- [ ] Age of Innocence
- [ ] Aguirre: The Wrath of God (Aguirre, der Zorn Gottes)
- [ ] A.I. Artificial Intelligence
- [ ] Airplane!
- [ ] Alexander Nevsky
- [ ] Alexander's Ragtime Band
- [ ] Alien
- [ ] Aliens
- [ ] All About Eve
- [ ] All About My Mother (Tobo Sobre mi Madre)
- [ ] All of Me
- [ ] All Quiet on the Western Front
- [ ] All That Heaven Allows
- [ ] All That Jazz
- [ ] All the President's Men
- [ ] Amélie
- [ ] American Beauty
- [ ] American in Paris, An
- [ ] American Werewolf in London
- [ ] Angel Heart
- [ ] Animal House
- [ ] Annie Hall
- [ ] Apartment, The
- [ ] Apocalypse Now
- [ ] Apollo 13
- [ ] As Good As It Gets

- [ ] Asphalt Jungle, The
- [ ] Attack!
- [ ] Audition
- [ ] Austin Powers: International Man of Mystery
- [ ] **B**ack to the Future
- [ ] Bad Company
- [ ] Ballad of Cable Hogue
- [ ] Ballad of a Soldier (Ballada o soldate)
- [ ] Band Wagon, The
- [ ] Barefoot in the Park
- [ ] Basic Instinct
- [ ] Batman
- [ ] Battleground
- [ ] Bedford Incident, The
- [ ] Belle de jour
- [ ] Bend of The River
- [ ] Ben-Hur
- [ ] Best Years of Our Lives, The
- [ ] Bicycle Thief, The (Ladri di Biciclette)
- [ ] Big
- [ ] Big Country, The
- [ ] Big Heat, The
- [ ] Big Lebowski, The
- [ ] Big Red One, The
- [ ] Big Sleep, The
- [ ] Billy The Kid
- [ ] Birds, The
- [ ] Blade Runner
- [ ] Blair Witch Project, The
- [ ] Blazing Saddles
- [ ] Bluebeard's Eighth Wife
- [ ] Blues Brothers, The

501 MUST-SEE MOVIES CHECKLIST

☐ Bonnie and Clyde
☐ Born Yesterday
☐ Braveheart
☐ Brazil
☐ Breakfast Club, The
☐ Breakfast at Tiffany's
☐ Bride of Frankenstein
☐ Bridge on the River Kwai, The
☐ Brief Encounter
☐ Bringing Up Baby
☐ Bullitt
☐ Burmese Harp, The (Biruma no tategoto)
☐ Butch Cassidy and the Sundance Kid
☐ Cabaret
☐ Camille
☐ Carrie
☐ Casablanca
☐ Catch-22
☐ Charade
☐ Charge of the Light Brigade, The
☐ Chicago
☐ Child's Play
☐ Children of Paradise (Les enfants du paradis)
☐ Chinatown
☐ Citizen Kane
☐ City of God (Cidade de Deus)
☐ Cleopatra
☐ Clockwork Orange
☐ Close Encounters of the Third Kind
☐ Come and See (Idi i smotri)
☐ Conversation, The
☐ Cross of Iron

- [ ] Crouching Tiger, Hidden Dragon (Wo Hu Cang Long)
- [ ] Cruel Sea, The
- [ ] **D**ances with Wolves
- [ ] Dangerous Liaisons
- [ ] Dark Star
- [ ] Das Boot
- [ ] Dawn of the Dead
- [ ] Day the Earth Stood Still, The
- [ ] Dead of Night
- [ ] Deer Hunter, The
- [ ] Deliverance
- [ ] Desert Fox, The
- [ ] Die Hard
- [ ] Dirty Dancing
- [ ] Dirty Dozen, The
- [ ] Dirty Harry
- [ ] Dr. Strangelove or: How I Learned to Stop Worrying and Love the Bomb
- [ ] Dr Zhivago
- [ ] Dog Day Afternoon
- [ ] Don't Look Now
- [ ] Do the Right Thing
- [ ] Double Indemnity
- [ ] Dracula (1958)
- [ ] Duck Soup
- [ ] Duel in the Sun
- [ ] **E**aster Parade
- [ ] Easy Rider
- [ ] 8^1/$_2$
- [ ] Enemy of the State
- [ ] English Patient, The
- [ ] Enter the Dragon

501 MUST-SEE MOVIES CHECKLIST

☐ Eraserhead
☐ E.T. The Extra-Terrestrial
☐ Everything You Always Wanted to Know About Sex
   (But were afraid to ask)
☐ Evil Dead
☐ Exorcist, The
☐ Fabulous Baker Boys, The
☐ Fahrenheit
☐ Fame
☐ Fargo
☐ Fatal Attraction
☐ Ferris Bueller's Day Off
☐ Fish Called Wanda
☐ Fitzcarraldo
☐ Five Graves to Cairo
☐ Fly, The
☐ Fog, The
☐ Forbidden Planet
☐ Forrest Gump
☐ Fort Apache
☐ Fortune Cookie
☐ Forty Guns
☐ 42nd Street
☐ Four Horsemen of the Apocalypse, The
☐ Freaks
☐ French Connection, The
☐ French Lieutenant's Woman, The
☐ Friday the 13th
☐ From Here to Eternity
☐ Full Metal Jacket
☐ Funny Face
☐ Funny Girl

- [ ] **G**andhi
- [ ] Gang's All Here, The
- [ ] Gay Divorcee, The
- [ ] General, The
- [ ] Gentlemen Prefer Blondes
- [ ] Ghost
- [ ] Ghost Busters
- [ ] Ghost of Mrs. Muir, The
- [ ] Gladiator
- [ ] Glengarry, Glen Ross
- [ ] Godfather, The
- [ ] Gold Diggers of 1933
- [ ] Goldfinger
- [ ] Gone with the Wind
- [ ] Good Morning, Vietnam
- [ ] Good, The Bad and The Ugly, The
- [ ] Goodfellas
- [ ] Graduate, The
- [ ] Grapes of Wrath, The
- [ ] Grease
- [ ] Great Escape, The
- [ ] Great Expectations
- [ ] Green Card
- [ ] Gremlins
- [ ] Greystoke: The Legend of Tarzan, Lord of the Apes
- [ ] Grosse Pointe Blank
- [ ] Groundhog Day
- [ ] Guess Who's Coming to Dinner
- [ ] Gunfighter, The
- [ ] Guns of Navarone, The
- [ ] **H**alloween
- [ ] Hard Day's Night, A

501 MUST-SEE MOVIES CHECKLIST

- [ ] Harold and Maud
- [ ] Harry Potter and the Philosopher's Stone
- [ ] Haunting, The
- [ ] Hell in the Pacific
- [ ] Hello, Dolly!
- [ ] High Noon
- [ ] High Plains Drifter
- [ ] High Society
- [ ] His Girl Friday
- [ ] Hombre
- [ ] Home Alone
- [ ] Hua yang nian hua (In the Mood for Love)
- [ ] Incredible Shrinking Man, The
- [ ] Independence Day
- [ ] In the Heat of the Night
- [ ] Invasion of the Body Snatchers
- [ ] In Which We Serve
- [ ] Iron Horse, The
- [ ] Italian Job, The
- [ ] It Happened One Night
- [ ] It's a Gift
- [ ] It's a Wonderful Life
- [ ] Jason and the Argonauts
- [ ] Jaws
- [ ] Jurassic Park
- [ ] Killing, The
- [ ] Killing Fields, The
- [ ] Kind Hearts and Coronets
- [ ] King of Comedy, The
- [ ] King and I, The
- [ ] King Kong
- [ ] Kiss of Death

- [ ] Kramer vs. Kramer
- [ ] La belle et la bête (Beauty and the Beast)
- [ ] Lady Eve, The
- [ ] La Grande Illusion (The Grand Illusion)
- [ ] Last Action Hero, The
- [ ] Last Emperor, The
- [ ] Last of the Mohicans, The
- [ ] Last Picture Show, The
- [ ] Last Train From Gun Hill
- [ ] Last Waltz, The
- [ ] Lawrence of Arabia
- [ ] Le dîner de cons
- [ ] Left-handed Gun, The
- [ ] Léon
- [ ] Les Diaboliques
- [ ] Les parapluies de Cherbourg (The Umbrellas of Cherbourg)
- [ ] Les Vacances de M. Hulot
- [ ] Letter from an Unknown Woman
- [ ] Life and Death of Colonel Blimp, The
- [ ] Life and Times of Judge Roy Bean, The
- [ ] Lion in Winter, The
- [ ] Little Big Man
- [ ] Little Caesar
- [ ] Little Shop of Horrors
- [ ] Lonely Are The Brave
- [ ] Longest Day, The
- [ ] Long, Hot Summer, The
- [ ] Long Riders, The
- [ ] Lord of the Rings: The Fellowship of the Ring, The
- [ ] Lost Horizon
- [ ] Lost in Translation

501 MUST-SEE MOVIES CHECKLIST

- [ ] Lost Weekend, The
- [ ] Love Story (1970)
- [ ] **M**ad MaX 2: The Road Warrior
- [ ] Magnificent Seven, The
- [ ] Maltese Falcon, The
- [ ] Man for All Seasons, A
- [ ] Manhunter
- [ ] Man of the West
- [ ] Man in the White Suit, The
- [ ] Man Who Shot Liberty Valance, The
- [ ] Man Who Would Be King, The
- [ ] Mary Poppins
- [ ] M*A*S*H
- [ ] Master and Commander: The Far Side of the World
- [ ] Matrix, The
- [ ] Mean Streets
- [ ] Meet Me in St. Louis
- [ ] Meet the Parents
- [ ] Memento
- [ ] Men in Black
- [ ] Metropolis
- [ ] Midnight
- [ ] Miller's Crossing
- [ ] Minority Report
- [ ] Misery
- [ ] Mission, The
- [ ] Mister Roberts
- [ ] Mr Smith Goes to Washington
- [ ] Modern Times
- [ ] Monty Python and the Holy Grail
- [ ] Moulin Rouge!
- [ ] Move Over, Darling

- [ ] Mummy, The
- [ ] My Darling Clementine
- [ ] My Fair Lady
- [ ] **N**aked Gun: From the Files of Police Squad, The
- [ ] Naked Lunch
- [ ] Naked Spur, The
- [ ] Napoléon
- [ ] Nashville
- [ ] Natural Born Killers
- [ ] New Leaf, A
- [ ] New York, New York
- [ ] Night of the Hunter, The
- [ ] Night of the Living Dead
- [ ] Nightmare on Elm Street
- [ ] Nine ½ Weeks
- [ ] North by Northwest
- [ ] Nosferatu
- [ ] Nothing Sacred
- [ ] Now, Voyager
- [ ] **O**dd Couple, The
- [ ] Officer and a Gentleman, A
- [ ] Oklahoma!
- [ ] Omen, The
- [ ] Once Upon a Time in the West (C'era una volta il West)
- [ ] One Flew over the Cuckoo's Nest
- [ ] On the Town
- [ ] On the Waterfront
- [ ] Others, The
- [ ] Out of Africa
- [ ] Outlaw Josey Wales, The
- [ ] Ox-Bow Incident, The
- [ ] **P**al Joey

501 MUST-SEE MOVIES CHECKLIST

- [ ] Papillon
- [ ] Passage to India, A
- [ ] Paths of Glory
- [ ] Patton
- [ ] Peeping Tom
- [ ] Phantom of the Opera, The
- [ ] Philadelphia Story, The
- [ ] Pillow Talk
- [ ] Pink Panther, The
- [ ] Pirates of the Caribbean: The Curse of the Black Pearl
- [ ] Planet of the Apes
- [ ] Platoon
- [ ] Player, The
- [ ] Point Blank
- [ ] Poltergeist
- [ ] Poseidon Adventure, The
- [ ] Pretty Woman
- [ ] Princess Bride, The
- [ ] Producers, The
- [ ] Professionals, The
- [ ] Psycho
- [ ] Public Enemy, The
- [ ] Pulp Fiction
- [ ] **Q**uiet Man, The
- [ ] **R**aging Bull
- [ ] Raiders of the Lost Ark
- [ ] Rain Man
- [ ] Raise the Red Lantern (Da hong deng long gao gao gua)
- [ ] Ran
- [ ] Random Harvest
- [ ] Rear Window
- [ ] Rebecca

- [ ] Rebel Without a Cause
- [ ] Red Badge of Courage, The
- [ ] Red River
- [ ] Red Shoes,
- [ ] Reservoir Dogs
- [ ] Ride the High Country
- [ ] Ride in the Whirlwind
- [ ] Rififi
- [ ] Right Stuff, The
- [ ] Ringu
- [ ] Rio Bravo
- [ ] Road to Morocco
- [ ] RoboCop
- [ ] Rocky
- [ ] Rocky Horror Picture Show, The
- [ ] Roman Holiday
- [ ] Romeo + Juliet
- [ ] Rome, Open City (Roma, città aperta)
- [ ] Rosemary's Baby
- [ ] Run of the Arrow
- [ ] Run Lola Run (Lola rennt)
- [ ] **S**afety Last
- [ ] Sands of Iwo Jima
- [ ] Saturday Night Fever
- [ ] Saving Private Ryan
- [ ] Scanners
- [ ] Scarface
- [ ] Schindler's List
- [ ] Scream
- [ ] Searchers, The
- [ ] Sergeant York
- [ ] Serpico

501 MUST-SEE MOVIES CHECKLIST

- [ ] Seven Brides for Seven Brothers
- [ ] Seven Samurai, The (Shichinin no samurai)
- [ ] Seventh Seal, The (Det sjunde inseglet)
- [ ] Shadow of the Vampire
- [ ] Shakespeare in Love
- [ ] Shane
- [ ] Shawshank Redemption, The
- [ ] She Wore a Yellow Ribbon
- [ ] Shining, The
- [ ] Shootist, The
- [ ] Shop Around the Corner, The
- [ ] Shoulder Arms
- [ ] Showboat
- [ ] Show People
- [ ] Silence of the Lambs, The
- [ ] Silent Running
- [ ] Singin' in the Rain
- [ ] Sixth Sense, The
- [ ] Sleeper
- [ ] Sleepless in Seattle
- [ ] Sleuth
- [ ] Solaris (solyaris)
- [ ] Some Like It Hot
- [ ] Sound of Music, The
- [ ] South Pacific
- [ ] Spartacus
- [ ] Speed
- [ ] Spider-Man
- [ ] Stagecoach
- [ ] StalaG 17
- [ ] Star is Born, A
- [ ] Star Trek: The Wrath of Khan

- [ ] Star Wars: Episode IV – A New Hope
- [ ] Sting, The
- [ ] Story of G.I. Joe, The
- [ ] Strangers on a Train
- [ ] Strike up the Band
- [ ] Sullivan's Travels
- [ ] Sunrise
- [ ] Sunset Boulevard
- [ ] Superman
- [ ] Sweet Smell of Success
- [ ] Tall T, The
- [ ] Taxi Driver
- [ ] Ten Commandments, The
- [ ] Terminator, The
- [ ] Texas Chain Saw Massacre, The
- [ ] There's Something About Mary
- [ ] They Were Expendable
- [ ] Thing, The
- [ ] Third Man, The
- [ ] This Is Spinal Tap
- [ ] Thomas Crown Affair, The
- [ ] Time Bandits
- [ ] Titanic
- [ ] To Be or Not to Be
- [ ] To Catch a Thief
- [ ] To Kill a Mockingbird
- [ ] Tootsie
- [ ] Top Gun
- [ ] Top Hat
- [ ] Tora! Tora! Tora!
- [ ] Total Recall
- [ ] Touch of Evil

501 MUST-SEE MOVIES CHECKLIST

- [ ] Towering Inferno, The
- [ ] Trading Places
- [ ] Traffic
- [ ] Train, The
- [ ] Treasure of the Sierra Madre, The
- [ ] Tremors
- [ ] Tron
- [ ] Troy
- [ ] True Grit
- [ ] True Lies
- [ ] Truman Show, The
- [ ] Twelve Monkeys
- [ ] Twelve O'Clock High
- [ ] 12 Angry Men
- [ ] 28 Days Later
- [ ] Two Rode Together
- [ ] 2001: A Space Odyssey
- [ ] **U**nforgiven
- [ ] Un homme et une femme
- [ ] Union Pacific
- [ ] Untouchables, The
- [ ] Usual Suspects, The
- [ ] **V**ertigo
- [ ] Vikings, The
- [ ] Village of the Damned
- [ ] Viva Las Vegas
- [ ] Von Ryan's Express
- [ ] **W**ages of Fear, The (Le Salaire de la peur)
- [ ] War and Peace
- [ ] War of the Worlds, The
- [ ] Waterloo
- [ ] Waterloo Bridge

- [ ] Way Out West
- [ ] Way We Were, The
- [ ] West Side Story
- [ ] Westworld
- [ ] Whatever Happened to Baby Jane?
- [ ] What's Up, Doc?
- [ ] When Harry Met Sally
- [ ] Where Eagles Dare
- [ ] While You Were Sleeping
- [ ] Wicker Man, The
- [ ] Wild Bunch, The
- [ ] Winchester '73
- [ ] Wings
- [ ] Witness
- [ ] Wizard of Oz, The
- [ ] Woodstock
- [ ] Wuthering Heights
- [ ] **X**-Men
- [ ] **Y**ankee Doodle Dandy
- [ ] Young Guns
- [ ] You Were Never Lovelier
- [ ] **Z**elig
- [ ] Zero Hour
- [ ] Zulu

First published in 2009 by Bounty Books,
a division of Octopus Publishing Group Ltd
2–4 Heron Quays, London E14 4JP
www.octopusbooks.co.uk

An Hachette UK Company
www.hachette.co.uk

ISBN: 978-0-753716-97-7

A CIP catalogue record for this book is available from the British Library

Printed and bound in China

Picture Credits:

Cover Photography: Photo12/Archives du 7eme Art

Inside Photography:

Photo12/Archives du 7eme Art 2, 9, 17, 25, 29, 45, 89, 101, 113, 121, 125, 143, 151, 163, 173, 189, 197, 205, 211; /Collection Cinéma 53, 65, 77, 133, 157, 221.